poems for children

Ashok Sawhny

gbd books

New Delhi, India.

FRUIT SALAD
Poems for Children
Copyright © Ashok Sawhny 2009

All Rights Reserved

ISBN 978 81 88951 56 7

First published 2009 by
ATHENA PRESS
Queen's House, 2 Holly Road
Twickenham TW1 4EG
United Kingdom

Published in India 2010 by
gbd books
I-2/16, Ansari Road, Daryaganj
New Delhi – 110002, INDIA
Email: generalbookdepot@yahoo.com
Ph.: 91 9810229648

Printed at Ajanta Offset and Packagings Ltd.

To my children,
Vipan, Ashok, Avinash, Radha, Meera, Jyoti and Geeta
and my grandchildren,
Shivani, Nandini, Raghav, Varun, Tarini, Dhruv.
Remember always: no greater riches or rewards will ever come your
way, nor can you aspire to anything greater, than to be able to live a
life of simple joys and happiness.

Contents

The Magical Island of Saturn

I'll tell you a story, my little children,
But I'll tell you this in rhyme,
I visited once the Isle of Saturn
Drinking Pepsi and lime.

Saturn is a magical island
With elves and fairies and all,
There was a low and a fairly high land
And the people were very tall.

Dwarfs were there but they were few
My fingertips were more,
And they had hair that never grew,
And this was part of folklore.

There was a school for little kids
And one for big ones too,
They had water jars without lids
And cows that didn't moo.

The cows were there for the milk
That the kids were made to drink;
Their skin was soft as satin and silk
And milk made the children think.

The kids could fly 'cos they had wings –
It's a magical island, remember –
Flying quickly through three golden rings
They never lost their temper.

The animals too could fly around
The elephant, giraffe and the donkey.
They played a match on a football ground
And the goalkeeper was the monkey.

The ball was always in the air
Flying from corner to corner,
A header was taken by the bear
As he was a fast learner.

There were lots of girls in there too,
Who had plenty of fun all day,
There was stitching and sewing and a dancing few,
And studying was by the way.

'Cos they were bright and very clever,
The boys they always beat,
They never skipped a class, but never!
Their homework was always complete.

Tailors and cobblers on the island,
Fruit sellers and shopkeepers too;
They gave each other a helping hand
And shared a common stew.

Dinner was always at seven o'clock
And for this they all sat down.
The doors were open, never a lock,
And all were invited from town.

A long loaf of brown bread
Happily fed them all,
They had no fear and no dread
There could ever be a shortfall.

Bread was both magical and free,
It could increase its size at will;
The king at the table and the queen, you see,
Would always pay the bill.

My story's done, but I can take you there
To the lovely Island of Saturn;
If you hold my hand we'll get somewhere
And see if we want to return.

Now read this poem and see if you find
The lessons you must learn.
It may tax a little your precious mind,
But now it's all your turn.

I Am the Moon

Tell me, children, tell me soon
Do you like a silvery moon?
She who lights the sky for you
And shows you all the stars too.

I am that moon, my little ones,
I like you with your dolls and guns,
I have two eyes and I can see
I love the way you look at me.

I grow in size, much like you,
You see me little and full too,
They call me crescent when I'm nearly half,
And when I'm old you can laugh.

Waves in the sea shimmer with me
We dance together whenever I'm free,
I always move from side to side
And from the sun I run and hide.

Dogs bark when they see me
I don't know why, 'cos I'm friendly,
I'm gentle and without ire –
Try the sun for brimstone and fire!

I'll say goodnight and keep you cool
So you can sleep then go to school,
If Toddler's Train* is where you go,
A grandfather's house is round the corner, you know.

---

* Toddler's Train is a nursery school in Sunder Nagar, New Delhi.

14

I Am the Sun

I know you kids don't like the sun
'Cos in the summer it isn't fun,
But when it's winter and cold outside
The sun is always on your side.

It takes those little shivers away
And makes you feel happy and gay;
I am that sun in the sky
And I can make the cold fly.

I cannot sleep during the day
And if the clouds are in my way,
I look for gaps for my ray
So you can go out and play.

Spare a thought for the trees and flowers
Enjoy yourself in the rain and showers;
Getting wet is lovely fun,
But catching a cold you must always shun.

I care for you, my little dears,
I can't bear to see your falling tears,
So keep a smile on your happy faces
As you study and run your races.

I Am a Tree

I am the tree you see in the park
On which there's perched a singing lark,
I'm big and strong and very wide
So you, my kids, can seek and hide.

Come winter, and I'm white as snow
But I come in varied colours, you know.
The reds, greens and the orange hues
Are colours that I never lose.

Come autumn, and you'll always find
I'm pretty as anything you have on your mind,
But then I have to shed my leaves
'Cos they can't stand the winter's freeze.

I'll surely bring them back for you –
As spring approaches that's what I'll do.
I love to see you swing about
But I'm scared you'll pull my branches out.

When you are feeling a little glum
Just climb on me and eat a plum,
Or try the apples and the pears
And don't worry about the neighbour's stares.

Did you know I breathe for you?
Both in and out, that's what I do.
What you breathe out is what I need –
Don't cut me down, you'll repent your greed.

You and I must live together
Through thick and thin and in every weather.
So when you grow up be kind to me
And I promise I'll be your good tree.

I Am a Rose

You know me as a flower – that's so,
But the rose, I'm not sure you know
That while colours I do not lack
I'm sometimes also very black.

I can be white and very fair,
Something like your granny's hair;
In your garden I can grow, my child,
But I'm happier when I'm in the wild.

I like my freedom, just like you,
I don't like being plucked – it hurts too,
I grow on bushes and also shrubs
And the morning dew gives me rubs.

I smell sweet, and that's that,
And look pretty without a hat.
There's some amongst us who aren't scented,
Though they're just as pretty and accented.

There are many names that I'm known by
But some may have escaped your roving eye.
There's Schoolgirl and Fairy Snow
And Grandpa Dickson and a Piccolo.

Now that you know so much about me
Go tell your grandpa and your granny;
They won't know how all this you knew
'Cos I've written this poem only for you.

I Am a Sailing Ship

Come on, kids, come for a ride –
I am a ship and I'm very wide.
I'm also very tall, you know,
And on my deck are masts that grow.

I sail the oceans and the seas
And go almost where I please;
I like the winds and the breeze
But in the Arctic I freeze.

We all know what icebergs are,
From them I stay very far.
Pretty they are, but they tear me asunder,
And I then simply go down under.

My men on board are very brave,
They manage with little and they don't crave,
There's lots of laughter all around
As waves make a deafening sound.

When the air is calm and the sun is out,
With clear blue skies and no winds about,
That's when they're all ready to shout
Sing and dance and eat some trout.

But when it begins to cloud over
And there's thunder and lightning from Calais to
    Dover,
Then I'm rocked from side to side
And there is no place where I can hide.

I am buffeted about like a little toy
Lost in the waves like a little boy,
Until the storm begins to abate
And all is well with the skipper and the mate.

Sometimes they take me from the sea
To the shores and dry-dock me,
Then look for things they have to do
To get me back to waters blue.
I don't mind the stops if they're now and then,
I'm off to sea and happy again.

I Am a Little Fairy Duck

I am a little fairy duck –
To kids I bring a lot of luck,
Come play with me and be my friends,
Let's travel together to Earth's ends.

I paddle on a crimson lake
Where you can come and pictures take –
Sketch, paint or simply look
Or read my lovely little book.

It's called the *Duck from Fairyland*,
Where all the ducks know how to stand
On one leg while the other is rested,
Body energy is never wasted.

This story is of a girl and a boy
Who came to the lake with an odd-looking toy.
It looked to me like it could fly,
Moving quickly much like I.

They called this toy an aeroplane –
Strange-looking bird with a windowpane,
I asked if it could fly like me,
They said, 'Let's try, let's see!'

They primed it up and spun the props,
I thought they were going to spray the crops.
I saw the plane sail through the air
And then there was water everywhere.

The crash was heard, loud and clear,
I was lucky I wasn't standing near.
The plane went down and was not seen again –
I saw the kids were in awful pain.

Their faces now were very grim,
I had to make it up to them,
'Come, let me take you for a ride,
I'm a flyer, so don't deride.'

On my back were two strange creatures,
Completely different, with no duck features.
I flapped my wings to keep from falling,
As the weight on my back was now appalling.

I flew them both with great gusto
To a fairyland called 'Hello-Hello',
Where ducks are white and also yellow,
And everyone sings, 'He's a jolly good fellow!'

The reference here is to our noble king
Who likes to wear a glossy ring;
He waddles like the rest of us
But sometimes takes the morning bus.

'Buses for ducks – you must be joking!'
The two kids say while alighting.
The king, you see, is a very old duck
And needs a bus 'cos he may run out of luck.

He rarely now comes out of his fort,
No longer interested in water sport;
He used to play water polo,
And even swam the Channel solo.

There were ducks in multicolour
Watching movies in Technicolor,
They would google too in their computers blue –
With so much info their heads just grew.

Fairy ducks, I told my crew,
Do everything that humans do.
We can write a very nice letter,
Jump and dive and swim much better.

Time now for them to go home
On a plane and away to Rome.
I don't know where they eventually got –
The king called me in 'cos it was very hot.

The Game of Tennis

You know Dennis the Menace,
But do you know the game of tennis?
You need a net, a racquet and ball,
And you need to be at least three-feet tall.

You toss the ball in the air
Then serve with Federer's flair.
If it doesn't come back the point is yours
And you improve your scores.

You're allowed to volley and to smash,
Lunge and plunge and also dash;
If you know how to slice, you can make it spin
But there's lines the ball must stay within.

Backhand, forehand, overhead, underhand –
These are shots that you can play,
Just keep the ball away from the stand
Or else you'll lose your way.

You can back your horse and lay your bet
For players are 'horses' too.
And then it's a matter of winning the set,
Then two more he'll have to do.

Now he's the champion with the cup in his hand
And glory all around,
Locks are OK with a broad headband,
And Borg can still astound.

The female version is more exciting
With great fashion on display,
There is some muscle, but very inviting
And the ladies can certainly play.

Martina will surely go down
As history's greatest player,
Until there is a new gal in town
Then we'll take it from there.

I hope, my children, you've enjoyed the game
And who knows? You might be the one to make a
name.

I Love Bananas

Unless there were twelve
I wouldn't eat them;
Bananas were my favourites
You can see that, ahem...

So a dozen were there
Ready at home,
As mother fed me stories
Of the elf and the gnome.

I'd come back from school
With hunger on the mind,
Imagine my state
If bananas I didn't find!

What is it with bananas
That drove me so,
Don't ask me, kids,
For I know you know.

They're lovely to eat
And filling too;
Try twelve bananas
And your day will be through.

When you peel the skin
Don't throw it around,
You'll leave folks aplenty
With their backs on the ground.

Bananas and cream
Was my ideal dream.
They grow in clusters
And are great stress-busters.

If twelve you can't eat
Choose the number you can;
Even three is a feat
And you're no less a man.

Enjoy the banana
As much as I do,
For the mind, it's manna –
Remember that too.

The Apple Tree

I've been asked to write about an apple tree
And the request has come from Tarini;
She is my little granddaughter, you know,
With lovely looks and locks that glow.

She is four-feet tall and all of seven,
Bit of a devil, but mostly heaven;
Something like an apple she is –
Golden, delicious – yes, she's bliss.

Apple trees grow in the hills;
They're fairly rugged, without frills.
The fruit they bear comes in different colours –
Reds, greens and gorgeous yellows.

If you eat at least an apple a day,
It will keep, they say, the doctor away;
The tree will be happy for it will be lighter –
Less weight to carry, and your face will be brighter.

Apple trees are not very tall
And you won't find them in a mall.
You'll have to climb to dizzy heights
But the orchards are delightful sights.

Orchards are gardens where we grow
Fruit trees – mostly apples, you know,
Some pears and plums and cherries too,
But mostly apple for the stew.

Birds are fond of the apple tree
'Cos they can peck on an apple, you see,
The tree though doesn't like this –
Don't tell the birds or they will lose bliss.

If you learn more about the apple tree
Please could you write and tell me?

The Three R's

Reading, writing and arithmetic…
My teacher is hypnotic.
School is my second home,
I love the building and its orange dome.

I go to class every day
And I let my teacher have her say,
So I can learn the three R's
To go home and count jam jars.

Then I can read what's on the jar
And remember to spell 'choco bar';
Physics and chemistry are too much for me
'Cos I'm only five and quite little, you see.

But I still need to read and also write
And count the number that I fight,
So my day is really not complete
Without me accomplishing the three R's feat.

The alphabet is a funny thing
I bet I know what's this alpha thing,
A precedes B and C, I can laugh –
Then there's D the E and the F's for enough.

But from A to Z I have to learn,
And without one, two and three, how will I earn?
And if I couldn't write,
How would this poem ever reach your sight?

And if you didn't know how to read and write
You wouldn't know who discovered the arc light;
If you couldn't count how many miles to go,
You'd keep Grandpa waiting at the door, you know.

So learn the three R's and you'll be glad –
You won't be illiterate and you won't be sad.

Why Do We Need Rain Clouds?

Tell me, what's a rain cloud?
Shh! Don't say it very loud,
It might suddenly start to rain,
And without a brolly that would be insane.

Then there are some that don't rain
And, therefore, don't cause pain.
Are these the ones that go drifting by
When I see a clear blue sky?

Why do clouds turn to black?
I like them white, so why not that?
Does anything ever ever gain
From clouds that bring the rain?

Yes, think of fields that would begin to cry,
Because lack of rain would make them dry.
How then would you get food to eat,
And respite from the searing heat?

There would be no leaves, the trees would be bare,
You wouldn't be able to breathe the hot air;
No tiger, lion, leopard or bear,
There would be famine and drought everywhere.

You wouldn't want that to happen, children,
So rain comes from above and is heaven.
So when you next see that big dark cloud,
Clap your hands and shout out loud!

Let the rain come pouring down,
And remove from your face that unhappy frown.
Isn't it lovely to see verdant trees,
And feel the cool of a morning breeze?

Granny

She'd make me sit on her knee
And look at me so lovingly;
That's what grannies generally do,
Unless you have been naughty and she finds you.

She used to tell me many a tale
Of pirates and the ships that sail,
Of thunder, lightning and ravaging storm,
Of what makes them leave hearth and home.

She would tell me stories of Robin Hood,
Of Tarzan, and how he bravely stood;
Of apes that roamed the jungle wild,
Hurricanes passed and the breeze was mild.

I heard great stories of mythology,
Of gods who strode the sky and the sea;
How history keeps on getting made,
As memories begin to gradually fade.

Of kings and queens and the common man,
Of streams of milk where water ran,
Of gnomes and fairies and goblins all,
Of the ten-mile-long waterfall.

She'd tell us the story of the doll with wings,
And of one who could fly through many rings,
A face that was fair with curly hair,
Like my sister, who was always there.

The doll would fly and my sister dance,
I always thought, what magic, what chance,
That a doll could fly like superman –
And soon I became the doll's fan.

She'd tuck me into bed sometimes,
And read to me some nursery rhymes,
Till I drifted off into gentle sleep –
To dream the dreams that I still keep.

She'd tell me of the gods above,
She'd do this with a lot of love,
I'd say a little prayer with her
Then she'd always say 'Goodnight, sir.'

'May you sleep well, my child,' she'd say,
'The night's for sleep, the day's for play;
School awaits you at the end of night,
And dawn will bring you joy and light.'

Grannies are all the same, you know;
They're there for us, but they may be slow.
She may not be able to run with you
On grass that's green and slippery too.

Love and respect your granny, you must;
She teaches you things like mutual trust.
Grandparents only know how to give you love,
And shower you with presents like rain from above.

My Toy Zoo

I have lots of lovely toys at home,
An elephant whose belly is like a dome,
A cuddly cat with whom I sleep
And a lizard that's a real creep.

I love my little teddy bear,
The one with lots of curly hair,
Brown, black, white and blue –
He's the favourite in my zoo.

There is a lion that doesn't roar
Only yawns and is a bit of a bore.
The tiger doesn't like the lion
But with the lion that's fine.

I also have a Donald Duck
And a Mickey Mouse that's run out of luck,
'Cos the cat doesn't like the little mouse
So my little zoo is a little madhouse.

No zoo is complete without the monkey –
And what about the black chimpanzee?
And those lovely South American birds,
With funny names and funny words…

The hippo beats the rhino blue;
There are reptiles, but very few,
No one likes the alligator –
Maybe I'll have to rusticate her.

My big black beauty is an Arabian horse,
I take him to a little racecourse.
He runs faster than me, that's how it
    should be –
For he's a horse and I'm a little me.

There's so much fun for girls and boys
When they play with their little toys.
'Come on, Daddy, be nice to me –
Come play with my toys, let's be happy.'

Let's Go to Music Land

Alice went to Wonderland,
But I'll take you where you can play in a band.
There's music to be made everywhere,
Have you ever been there?

There'll be drums, flutes and pianos too,
And you can choose what you want to do:
Sing your favourite nursery rhyme
Or dance to music in double-quick time.

Play the violin, if you like
Or the castanets on a mountain bike –
No one cares what's in your hand,
'Cos you, my children, are in Music Land!

It's very close to you, you know,
It's not even a stone's throw
From the beating of your tiny heart,
'Cos that's where music makes a start.

Music must have an inner ring,
Only then can you really sing,
And it doesn't matter if you're out of tune
Everyone is because it's hot in June.

I've brought you now to the place to be –
Music for all, and happiness for free.
Sing or play as you will,
Enjoy the music, and have your fill.

Prayer

Put your little hands together,
Hold them up to the sky,
Make a wish, say a prayer,
And God will listen on high.

For he lives there beyond the blue,
Looking down at all of you.
Your prayers will be answered – here's a clue:
He loves his children and loves them true.

He'll grant you what you honestly wish
But only when he thinks it's fair;
For you cannot ask for another's dish,
For others you must care.

Ask for happiness, ask for love,
He'll give you more than you know.
Ask for rain from above,
And he'll also give you snow.

He showers us all with his blessings,
On his mercy do we live,
When you eat your food and your puddings,
Your thanks to him you must give.

He'll make you big and also strong,
And pretty and fair too;
He'll teach you right from the wrong,
And tell you what is true.

So remember God and say your prayer,
And never ever weep,
For while you're dreaming he'll be there,
To look after you as you sleep.

I Love my Toys

I have lots of toys in my home
There's an elf, a doll and a silvery gnome;
I love to play with my toys,
More than I do with girls and boys.

I like my cat and my dog,
I also have a little hog,
A jumbo too, with a flapping ear,
Toyland's incomplete without spotted deer.

I really don't like crocodiles,
But I love the monkeys with their impish smiles.
My toys are made from different stuff,
In different colours, including buff.

The two-humped camel I like the most:
When he's hungry I give him toast,
Dinner is always roasted lamb;
Pigs are my friends so there is no ham.

I have a lion with a handsome mane,
He charged a window and broke a pane,
My Siberian tiger roars like mad,
And all my toys think that's very bad.

Once a week I have a feast –
My toys and I and the local priest –
We say a prayer and seek his blessings,
Then tuck in till we finish the puddings.

My toys are my world, you see,
I'm lost without them and they without me.
We do the weirdest things together,
And are always happy playing with each other.

The Two Old Men and their Crazy Zoo

I'll tell you a story of two old men
Who kept two elephants and one hen.
When they came back from an elephant ride,
The hen couldn't find a place to hide.

So she went between the elephants' legs
And promptly laid a dozen eggs.
The old men were happy until they saw
The cat of the alley raise its paw.

A battle now was looming large,
The old men began to look for a barge
To flee the magical island of war,
Before the cat into the elephant tore.

The hen was kind of a laid-back hen –
She could write her name with a fountain pen.
Tell me what pen has to do with fountain,
And I'll tell you what snow has to do with mountain.

Enough of nonsense is always enough,
And there's also a limit to the amount you can bluff,
So we're back to the story of the two old men
Who lived in a shack they called their 'den'.

How old do you think the old men were?
One was called Martin and the other just 'Sir'.
A hundred plus they were, for sure,
And having got there they wanted more.

Lest we forget the hen and the cat,
The cat was out to get the rat;
When she saw the elephant, she ran like hell –
Remember the old ding-dong bell?

The pussy was now in the well,
And the hen, she thought she had a story to tell,
So she told the elephants what she knew
But the old men and the elephants hadn't a clue.

They tried to pull the pussy out,
They did all they could, bar a big shout,
The cat then made a gigantic effort
And out of the well she came like a rocket.

The rat was given a merry chase,
Which soon became an obstacle race.
The elephants always in the way,
Slow on their feet with nothing to say.

They were pecked on their heads by the flying hen,
And pushed and pulled by the two old men,
And nothing seemed to come of it
Until the cat was by the rat bit.

All hell broke loose in the island zoo:
The hen became a goose, and that's true.
The situation now was very grim,
So the old men told the rest of them
To leave the island and go to Greece –
And hope that somehow they'd find peace.

'Age is all in the mind,' they said,
As from the island they finally fled:
Elephants, cat, rat and the men –
Only left behind was a lonely goose hen.

This is the end of the story, my children,
Of the magic you can weave with imagination,
Stars you can pluck from the sky –
And to boredom you can say goodbye.

Snow

Have you seen falling snowflakes,
Icy winds and frozen lakes?
Have you seen grass turn white?
It really is a beautiful sight.

When you play in the snow
Make a snowman with a bow.
On his head put a red hat,
Make him thin or make him fat.

It's very cold when it snows
Colder still when the wind blows,
Your cheeks will turn red and lips chap,
Make sure you have enough woollen wrap.

Snow looks lovely on Christmas trees,
You feel so fresh in the morning breeze.
If you have never ever seen snow,
Ask Mum and Dad and to the hills go.

Robin Hood

Sitting by the fireside
With burning logs of wood,
I went back to those good old days
To the times of Robin Hood.

He was my hero, without doubt,
And all that mattered to me
Was to see Errol Flynn and then to shout
When he swung from tree to tree.

The arrow was never off its mark
And of that I was sure;
If mattered not if it was forest or park
'Cos I couldn't have asked for more.

There was nothing little about the John I knew
Or the staff he carried around;
Robin got beat but only by a few,
And John had him pinned to the ground.

A lovely maid was Marian,
And she was Robin's girl;
He went through castle and gates of iron
To take Marian for a whirl.

Richard was King and also Crusader,
And a pretender was on the throne;
Brother's keeper was he, brother!
All trust turned to stone.

Sherwood Forest will always stay
In every romantic's mind,
As the place where Robin would rest and play
Then share out the spoils left behind.

The Beggar

You've seen him, children, on the street
When he comes to you and asks for alms;
He may not have shoes on his feet
But he will always have open palms.

He is the one who needs our kindness
And our help with what we can;
So look upon him with some fondness,
For he is after all a man.

You are lucky, you can get to school,
Buy your books and study well;
He is like you, he's not a fool –
He can also stories tell.

But his parents couldn't afford a school
So he didn't learn to read and write,
He never sat on a classroom stool
And that's a sorry plight.

Don't look down upon him,
Don't make him feel small,
Give him a smile if you have nothing else,
Cheer him up so he doesn't fall.

Fire

I like your colours
And your glow,
I like it when
You're burning slow.

Fire, O fire, you are divine!
You give me warmth,
And I feel fine.

You keep me from the bitter cold,
Without you there'd be misery untold,
My favourite dish you help me cook,
And by your side I read a book.

You are a very lovely sight,
When it's dark you are my light,
Fire, O fire, keep burning bright
Show me the way through the night!

But keep yourself within check,
For all your ravaging leaves you a wreck,
Your temper then knows no bounds
As you tear through hills and scorch the grounds.

I hate to have to put you out,
For you give me relief from my gout.
All said and done, you're a lovely thing,
As good cheer is what you really bring.

Father Christmas

There's snow around, it's wintry too –
The skies are clear and nice and blue,
It's Christmas time – you all know me,
I'm Father Christmas, don't you see.

You know me from the robes I wear,
The colour's red, and white my hair,
I carry my shopping bags with me,
I have in them what brings you glee.

Light, at first, a candle of hope
So you, my children, can learn to cope,
If you're unhappy with what you get
Hope will set your mind at rest.

You'll always think of the next time round
When maybe your joys will know no bound;
I'll leave you with your presents for now,
Merry Christmas – I'll take a bow!

Why Must I Never Lie?

Why must I never lie?
'Cos these words came from the sky.
God lives up on high,
And so I must never lie,

If I came last in my class
Or broke Mum's favourite looking glass,
And what if I didn't pass?
I'd still be eating food not grass.

I get scared and so I lie
And to truth I say goodbye,
And when I'm caught I simply cry,
So why did I have to tell a lie?

To lie is such an easy thing
But it will only shame bring;
Lies always have a hollow ring
And truth will always be king.

When I sit for my exam
And I'm asked a question by ma'am,
Why should I try and bluff
And not just say how sorry I am?

Love your Teacher

You go to school every day
For five days a week,
Not far from home, you know the way,
And knowledge is what you seek.

You want to learn to read and write
And to be able to speak well,
To know the difference between wrong and right,
And stories be able to tell.

Someone has to teach you this
And correct you when you're wrong;
Simple things are always bliss
If in your heart there is a song.

Teachers are next only to God
For they teach you all you know,
Even of Scripture and the Lord –
You learn all this as you grow.

So give your teacher love and respect
And the teacher will be happy too;
You'll not only learn what is cause and effect,
But also why the skies are blue.

My Tiger, My Horse

I like fairy cakes and strawberry jam,
Bacon, sausage and cold ham,
Bananas and cream on the side
As Tiger and I then go for a ride.

Tiger is my favourite horse,
We canter along, avoiding gorse,
Through meadows and the flowing plains –
My umbrella with me if it rains.

I am seven while Tiger is four
But he's always eating and wants more.
Grass is what Tiger likes to eat
And that for a tiger is a funny feat.

He's kind and gentle and caring for me,
'Specially when we're approaching a tree;
Walking around at an easy pace
He knows we're not in a horsey race.

Parents

Parents are why we're here on earth –
Mum and Dad who gave us birth,
They care for us, they bring us up,
They help us grow, they make us sup.

From the moment of our first bawl
Through many stages, as we learn to crawl,
They're there for us, for now and ever,
Ties that we will cherish for ever.

We respect and we love them too
For all the troubles that they go through,
To teach us what the world is about
To gently speak and not to shout.

Parents are like God for us,
We thank them for their love and fuss;
We wish them long and happy lives
And hope we become just as wise.

God bless our parents.

The Three-legged Race

My friend and I ran at great pace,
Tied together in a three-legged race,
We stumbled and fell but got up again –
Scratches and bruises on me and Ben.

We sped towards the halfway line,
When someone fell with a friend of mine;
We laughed at them as we moved on,
For them the race was as good as gone.

Three-quarters down the racing track,
Wishing we'd never joined this pack.
'Too late to think,' said Ben to me,
'Let's plod on till we're set free.'

The end of the race was now in sight
And so was our will to run and fight.
Our joy knew no bounds for now,
We'd run the race, so we'd take a bow.

We'd done our best and run quite fast,
The finishing line was now well passed.
There's a lesson in this, dear children of mine,
Never give up till the finishing line!

What Would it be Like to be a Flower?

What would it be like to be a flower –
Waiting for the sun to bloom,
For the rain to fall in a heavenly shower?
I wondered, looking out from my room.

My petals red, my stalk so green,
For I'm a rose, you see;
I won't lose any of my lovely sheen,
And my heart is full of glee.

The sun shone ever so bright,
As I saw my fellow rose
All spruced up, a collector's delight,
As a gardener came in with a hose.

I was tidied up and watered well,
Happy as a lark with life,
With many a lovely story to tell,
Till I spied a lady with a knife…

Filled now with anguish and dread,
I felt the end was in sight,
Pale and yellow from a radiant red,
I knew dark would now be my night.

I wished and hoped she'd leave me alone,
But the look in her eyes said 'no'.
I shook and quivered, turning to stone,
If only she'd let me go!

She passed me by with never a glance,
Seeming interested no more.
Wasn't I happy to have escaped the lance,
As into my friends she tore?

Never mind, friends, it's the fate of all,
Of all who live on earth:
The end is there, even kings will fall,
And that holds for all given birth.

The reverie over, I asked again,
Why can't I be as I am?
What is it with the world of men?
'Cos honey can never be strawberry jam.

I'd Like to Be...

A pilot is what I'd like to be,
And a bomber's what I'll fly,
That's my dream for the little me,
And I'll go zoom in the sky.

An engine driver's another choice,
Since a train's such lovely fun,
I like the whistle, I like the voice,
And the way it shines in the sun.

I've also dreamt of driving a car,
Imagine a 'Rolls' for me!
Liveried up, me the chauffeur,
In the rear, My Lord and Lady.

I'd like to be a General,
Maybe Chief of the Army Staff;
I know the job's ephemeral,
But the General has the last laugh.

I could also be an actor,
For that's what I do in class,
When I don't know addition from factor,
I tell my dad, 'Don't worry – I'll pass!'

Climbing is also a passion,
To put a flag atop a hill,
Wearing gumboots or whatever's in fashion,
I'm Tenzing, so I won't pay the bill.

Soccer is the modern rage,
With lots of money too.
Remember Maradona on the front page –
Who cares if Maradonas are few?

I could also be a Tiger,
No, not what you see in the zoo,
This guy's a jolly good golfer,
And might run for President too.

And what about Headmaster,
Maybe in my own school.
I shan't let boys run after
The girls and play the fool.

Maybe I'll just be Prime Minister,
There's really nothing to do,
For my deputy I'll appoint my sister,
And we'll take turns going to the loo.

Finally I'd like to be just me,
And hope I'm big and tall,
So I can take care and be happy,
And not worry about a fall.

Fruit Salad

I am the original make-up artist
With pears and plums and apples for you,
Let's take a walk in the morning mist,
My orchard's there for the plucking too.

All the ingredients that you need,
To have me as your dish,
Are on the trees that grow from seed,
And can be yours if you wish.

Mix and match the sweet with citrus,
Orange, banana and the juicy grape.
Eat at table or in the bus,
Share with friends, or they will gape.

You can either have me as I am,
Or do the same with cream,
Add, if you like, some cake and jam,
And I'd be your heavenly dream.

I wait for you in a crystal bowl,
All sliced and ready to eat,
I taste so good I'll touch your soul,
Now isn't that a treat!

Tarzan the Apeman

You've heard of me, haven't you, children?
I was known as the apeman,
Born in the jungle and raised to win,
Swinging from tree to tree as only I can.

My friends were the best of beast and man,
The chimp, the croc and gorilla,
We jumped and played and also ran,
The rafts our little flotilla.

Our language was not as you know it,
And names were not for us,
The calls of the wild were learned bit by bit,
And friends we became thus.

Jane was my jungle friend
But she couldn't speak like me,
And yet we moved from end to end,
She was a lovely sight to see.

I hope I remain forever in your minds,
As Tarzan the apeman,
For love it is that always binds,
Man to beast to man.

The Village Square

Not far from home was the village square,
Fruits were there, and so was the bear,
Jacket potatoes and their hawkers alike,
Beckoning all to come have a bite.

Everyone gathered to sell their wares,
To have some fun and eat some pears,
To buy some trinkets to take back home,
Then tell your friends they came from Rome.

Newspaper vendors and mags galore,
'Come buy this lot – I've got some more,
Have to sell before the day's done,
For then I'll be looking at the homeward run.'

'Half-price suits and matching ties,
All from Harrods – not telling lies;
Floral hats for the lovely madam,
Come on, man, be a kindly Adam.'

'Toys and balloons and chewing gum,
It's not all for kids, there's also rum;
Merry-go-rounds and the Ferris wheel,
Look under my curtain and I'll take your reel.'

There's a joker somewhere in the pack,
And a horse to ride also known as the hack,
A Sunday stroll through the village square,
It's fun, it's a frolic, it's a lovely fair.

Come join me on a sunny Sunday,
And I'll take you for a bicycle ride.
I may not even lose my way,
If you're the one by my side.

The Sparrow

I twitter, I chirp, I flap my wings,
I love to hear the bell that rings,
I am the sparrow on your lawn,
I am small and my colour's fawn.

I see you sip your morning tea,
I look for things that please me;
The little things I pick from grass,
I do with elegance, ease and class.

I keep to myself as I hop around
Until another morsel I've found,
And then it's time for the ravenous me
To have my breakfast, as you have your tea.

I see a paper in your hands,
Spots, blotches and strange-looking strands,
I am not sure what you do with it,
'Cos seemingly you just sit, sit, sit!

I'm scared of you 'cos I'm so small,
You seem so big, so very tall.
Thank God you can't scale the heights I do –
For what would I do if you also flew?

So I'll see you tomorrow, my 'paper friend',
I hope our friendship will never end,
Maybe I'll try your tea some day,
If you promise to try living my way.

Laugh if you Can

It's barren, it's dry, it's Cadbury Fry,
Chillies in the sand that make me cry,
Camels on horseback, what a funny little world,
Careful, else from a doll's house you'll be hurled.

It's crazy, it's man that makes me sad,
Smiles on faces that don't seem glad,
Tears in the eyes and plenty of sighs,
The land very flat, and hills that don't rise.

If it's nonsense you like, come ride my bike,
We'll flag down cars and hitch-hike,
And if that ain't enough, we'll pick up some stuff,
Then march down the road that ain't too rough.

We'll go past the roses and strike all the poses,
And try not to run over any running noses,
'Cos we don't like the cold and we do what we're
    told,
But if you aren't beautiful, I can't be bold.

So let's cut out the crap and forget the mousetrap,
The cat was named Agatha, and she never took the
    rap.
Poirot was the guy, the mastermind,
And he wasn't good if a rat you had to find.

You should have knocked on Sherlock's door,
His Holme's at the corner, the corner's no more;
He would have detected the rat for you,
And, with a little bit of luck, its grandfather, too.

I know you can't laugh at the nonsense I write,
But how about laughing at your own sorry plight,
Having to read this rubbish of mine,
Simply because it looks divine!

A Flower

There's a fairy I knew who loved, much as I do,
Your colours, your beauty and the rainbow's hue.

Flower, O flower, where will I find another like you?
From smiling gardens to rolling hills,
Swaying roses and dancing daffodils,

From bud to bloom, you are a joy to watch,
By the river's edge or on the ledge,
By the mountainside, among heather and fern,
I see so much, so much do I learn
Of nature and you, of birds and the dew,
Of the morning sun that awakens you.

The scent of your petals is almost divine –
I wish you were mine, only mine.
Alas! You are there for all to share,
Nature's gift for us all everywhere.
Blessings on us you must shower,
Bloom for ever, O lovely flower.

Bumblebee

Buzz as it does and hums away too,
The bumblebee in the morning dew.
The sun seeks to rise,
In a morning's surprise,
And night falls away,
Making way for the day,
And the bumblebee is on its way.

Hovering around,
Not covering much ground,
Flowers it seeks
To smell around.

And colours to see,
In its flights of fancy,
As it bumbles along
In its heart there's a song –
A song called the song of life.

Sing it as you will
Sing it till you're still.
Flit like the bumblebee,
Hop from tree to tree.

Gather what you can
In life's short span.
Buzz like the bee
And then make way
For the next man.

The Lion King

I am the King
Of all that I survey;
Nothing ever gets in my way.

I live in the open,
I live in the wild,
My manner is both gentle and mild.

People get me wrong:
Just because I am strong,
It doesn't mean I am hostile.

I have friends in the park,
From the elephant to the lark,
And they all seem to like my style.

I do not like to lose,
But I am gracious in defeat,
And that is no mean feat.

I am King of the Jungle,
I like to mingle
With my subjects, big and small.

They seek my protection,
With love and affection –
And a bit of fear, as well.

My roar after a feast
Shakes both man and beast,
And they run for cover, like hell.

My day is now over,
I now rest in clover,
And it is time for me to sleep.

Birds and Me

I saw nothing.
I sensed it all.
That's when I felt
So very small.

When the birds came into view,
Flying higher than I knew,
There was something mighty in those little ones –
Something magical in their swooping runs.

Their constant chirp and little chatter
Meant nothing to me, and did not matter:
They were there flying together
Happy in the midst of each other.

The sky was theirs, the Earth to see
And then there was this little bit of me.
'Look up, not down,' they seemed to say.
'That little speck is not in our way.'

He walks the Earth
He flies around
He thinks he has
The ultrasound.
No moon's too far,
For him to go,
He's lost his way on Earth, you know.

Jack and Jill

Moments in life and moments in time,
Moments both beautiful and sublime,
Remember the story of Jack and Jill,
A magical little nursery rhyme.

Jack fell down and broke his crown
Jill came down without a frown;
Life is a walk on uneven ground,
You will be up, you will be down.

Treat them both in equal measure,
You will not, then, repent in leisure,
And soon enough you'll realise
Life is indeed a wonderful treasure.

Hickory, Dickory, Dock

Hickory, dickory, dock,
The mouse ran up the clock,
The clock struck one –
School is great fun,
Walk to class, don't run.

It's raining, it's pouring,
The old man is snoring –
When you enter your class,
You must wish your teacher 'Good morning'.

Humpty Dumpty sat on a wall,
Humpty Dumpty had a great fall –
Some you won't like and some won't like you,
But you must try to be friends with all.

Ding, dong, bell,
Pussy's in the well –
Whatever you have to tell,
Tell it nicely, don't yell.

Mary had a little lamb,
Its fleece was white as snow –
Bread and butter and a little jam,
Is what you need to grow.

Itsy-bitsy spider,
Climbed up the water spout –
Every horse needs a rider,
Every sulk a pout.

Baa baa, black sheep,
Have you any wool?
Promises you have to keep,
And don't give me that bull.

Sing a song of sixpence,
A pocket full of rye –
Laugh, if you will, at my expense,
But never tell a lie.

Jack and Jill went up the hill,
To fetch a pail of water –
If you spend, you pay the bill,
And you must never falter.

Mickey Mouse and Donald Duck,
Walt Disney's creations –
You will sometimes run out of luck,
But never run out of patience.

Tables

Two times two is always four,
And three times three is nine.
Why are we not always sure?
Why is man in decline?

Four times four is sixteen,
And five times five, twenty-five.
Why can't I just stay a teen?
Why not forever alive?

Six times six is thirty-six,
Seven times seven, forty-nine.
Who said life isn't a heady mix
And the world simply divine?

Eight times eight is sixty-four,
And nine times nine, eighty-one,
There is not now much more to go,
And a hundred can't be much fun.

Circus

I saw a circus as a child,
Animals were anything but wild;
The joker was the greatest fun,
And he did not even have a gun.

Monkeys flying on the trapeze,
Eating chillies and green peas,
Cats and dogs doing their thing,
Every performer out to please.

Magnificent elephants ambling down,
Chimpanzees wearing lovely crowns,
Laughter, laughter everywhere –
And amid all this the inimitable clown.

Horses trotting in majestic style,
Walking out in single file,
Not a beauty out of step,
Poetry in motion for a while.

Lion and whips and tamers galore,
Fun and games for all, for sure,
Old and young and babes in arms,
Simple joys and happiness pure.

Men and animals – artists all,
Varied creatures, big and small;
Different things move different people,
The circus moves one and all.

A Child's Journey

Chirpy from the time it's born,
Lying awake from night to morn,
You can say goodbye to sleep,
Revise arithmetic – count the sheep!

Wonder in those little eyes,
Constant element of surprise,
Everything so startling and new,
Beginning a journey with no end in view.

Nappies, nannies and all who care,
Looking at the truly rare,
Happy in its little cot,
Playing with a teddy bear.

Crawling, stumbling, falling baby,
Testing patience and skills, maybe,
Making it up with a toothless smile,
Grinning eyes and a lot of guile.

Two steps, three steps, then some more,
Growing up ain't a chore –
Toddler now, trying the walk,
With grandma's finger and baby talk.

Walking leads to running shoes,
Always looking for little clues,
'Tell me what's for dinner, Mama!'
Hope it's ham, and trust it's Parma.

Music now is in the air,
Nursery rhymes seem so fair,
Seashells and jingle bells,
Christmas round the corner, everyone yells.

Time for school and the carpool,
Less time now to play the fool,
Study now is serious stuff,
A waiting ma'am to call your bluff.

One to ten is simple arithmetic,
Numbers beyond abstract and mathematic,
Who said Einstein was terribly bright?
Why did he not invent the tube light?

Lovely, innocent, precocious child,
Gentle mostly, sometimes wild,
Chasing splendid butterflies,
Speech confined to telling no lies.

Frocks give way to skirts, you know,
Girls meet boys as they grow,
The child you knew is left behind,
Creatures now of a different kind.

Leaving home for boarding school,
Water polo in the swimming pool;
Stepping out into adulthood –
Maid Marian and Robin Hood.

Don't lose this memory, not for a while,
Not even when you're old and senile;
You may not remember the child that was you,
But don't ever forget, from there you grew.

Dolls and their Pretty Houses

I wondered at the pains he was taking;
Mum was busy with cakes she was baking.
O doll's house, there'd be no you without my dad,
You were there and I was glad.

The fun we had, just you and I,
Dreams I dreamt, on them to fly
To distant lands, my doll and I,
Between the laughter and the cry.

You were my kingdom, my universe,
I was the Queen, with a full purse.
Beautiful was the maid with me,
My little doll she set me free.

Pins and frocks and dainty shoes,
To drive away the morning blues,
Dressing her up so she didn't fall,
Looking pretty for the evening ball.

Growing up was never in mind,
Happy I was with one of my kind,
You were my palace, my royal den,
I loved you dearly, my pet playpen.

Living around the two of you,
My home, my friend, ever so true,
What else could I have asked for –
There being no need for anything more?

Girls and dolls forever together,
Birds they are of the same feather,
Gentle as gentle can ever be;
But beware the sting, remember Queen Bee.

Anjali

Your grandfather said you are Anjali,
Ten years old with a heart of gold,
And you like writing poetry...
So here is something you may not have been told.

Poetry comes from the heart
The mind has little to do with it;
You must *feel* for a start,
Only then will your lines be lit.

With warmth, feeling and your soul,
With laughter, sadness and everything,
We are not just a sum of parts, we are whole:
Your poems will then happiness bring.

Write, my child, when you feel like writing
Not when you have to write,
There is nothing more inspiring
Than the human spirit and its fight.

You love your doll
So write about it;
You see rain fall,
Let your eyes describe it...

Remember, Anjali, to love life,
To love the people you meet,
Because then you will live without strife
And a happy life will be at your feet.

Send me your poems, my little one,
Show me the heart you've put in them,
Make them light, make them fun –
Who knows, you may be a poetic gem.

Some of the above you may not understand,
But that's not important:
Poet to poet is a message from me,
My dear Anjali, keep writing.

The Lollipop

When you lick a lollipop,
Don't think, don't ever stop,
The taste so good, the colour too…
You have no idea what it will do for you.

Sweet things will come to mind
Your childhood you may also find;
It's fun to be grown-up, I guess,
But greater fun is in the lick and the mess.

When you have licked the lollipop, then lick what's
    left,
With a lick of the stick, the mind's bereft
Of the cares and worries of everyday life,
Of the struggles and battles and constant strife.

See how simple life can be:
The humble lollipop can make you merry.
You may then want to lick some more
Or like a lion, simply roar.

If it doesn't do all this for you
I'll tell you what, I'll give you a clue:
Go get yourself a walking stick,
Or put your head under a brick!

Three cheers then, for you, lollipop!
Good for Mum and also Pop,
And good for the guy who makes them, you know,
'Cos he's the one who makes the dough.

Dough is bread, examine your head;
Who wants dough under the bed?
Give me a lollipop, and you take the dough –
I'll get more happiness than you'll ever know!

Butterfly

I see the lovely spotted wings,
I see the beauty of those rings;
Come hither, little butterfly,
Spare me a moment as you go by.

I've often looked at you in awe,
Wonderstruck by what I saw.
I've chased you down the garden slope,
You with your wings and I a skipping rope.

I have seen you from near and afar,
Flitting as you do from flower to flower,
The riot of colour that is you,
The yellow, the orange and the blue.

I've caught you with my fingers too,
I hope I didn't hurt you,
It was only to get a closer view
Of the winged fairy that I knew.

I wish you could in a swarm fly,
So I could see you up on high,
Rainbow colours across the sky...
Why only blue? Why, oh why?

What made you light and oh so bright?
Why aren't you visible at night?
Imagine a duet of you and the stars,
A flutter, a twinkle and those vanishing hours.

Those wondrous designs on your back,
So different from the flying pack;
A flower is all that you need,
To bear the brunt as you feed.

Magical it is, little butterfly,
To see you in the fields of rye;
I see you as a flying flower,
For that is what to me you are.

I'll race you down the fields one day,
I'll run straight, you'll lose your way,
'Cos you have many friends to greet,
And say hello to each flower you meet.

You look so different in the wild,
The greatest joy for a child,
Part of wondrous nature, you
Have striking patterns and vivid hue.

May I always see you around,
Living as you do close to the ground,
Flying onto my empty lap,
If I'm dozing or having a nap.

The Royal Cat

Good morning is a *meow* for me
As I wake up sleepy-eyed, you see,
Ginger steps and one big yawn,
I am the cat, and my colour's fawn.

My day begins in someone's lap,
Gentle stroking, no clap, no slap,
I pout, I smile and I purr
For my lady is wearing silky fur.

My milk arrives in porcelain jars,
I move around in fancy cars,
I am the royal pet, you see –
The Queen, she is a busy bee.

I'm careful not to step on her gown
Lest milady gives me the royal frown,
'Cos I'm always in tow, you see –
Wherever she goes, I go for free.

I am a very lucky cat –
Don't need to go looking for fat.
No mice for me, 'cos I'm nice, you see –
They have the traps, so they don't need me!

There's fun and frolic all around for me,
I come, you see, from the tiger family;
I look like them, only smaller maybe,
That's why they can't and I can climb a tree.

I have a few kittens
And they wear mittens,
We all go to Ascot, and you know why
'Cos I'm the royal cat on the sly.

Dumbo Jumbo out on Safari

Jumbo is my real name
Who called me an elephant?
Dumbo is what gets me fame,
Even if I am the sycophant.

Remember, you were on my back
As I swayed to and fro,
I took you where there was no track
Just because you had to go.

You were on a safari hunt,
The tiger squarely on your mind,
Because of me and my punt
Your quarry I was able to find.

Time for padding softly through
Breaking leaves and the grass,
Lying low as the growl grew;
Let danger go, let it pass.

That was not to be you see
'Cos you were on a crazy trip,
I was left to fend for me
Your gun you thought was the whip.

You fired a shot, the crack I heard,
Hurry, scurry and a lightning flash;
There was neither man nor bird –
All I heard was a mighty crash.

The worst is what I expected
Trumpeting, I charged like hell,
Till I saw and realised
'Twas not tiger, but you that fell!

The hunt was over, and I in clover –
Dreams shattered but life intact,
From Calais to the cliffs of Dover
The tiger and I had a pact.

We are the best of friends, you see.
I may quiver but he shivers too.
Have you never seen a grinning me?
Especially when he's caged in the zoo.

The Monkey and I

I am the clown in my town
And I never wear a frown,
My nose is red and there's a hat on my head
I'll make you laugh till you feel you're dead.

I'll cycle in with a monkey on a rack,
He's my friend, and very laid-back,
We do things together you'd never imagine –
He has the upper hand, but he'll never win.

'Cos the things we do are the things I know,
Which my friend don't know, so he is naturally slow.
Imagine the monkey doing the trapeze –
He may go up and not come down, if you please.

But the star of the show is my dear friend,
He has four legs and a red rear end,
He plucks lice from the head of mice
And doesn't like it much when I say, 'Not very nice!'

His antics are funny and simply divine
And the way he moves he could be floating on the Rhine.
So if he's the star, what am I?
I'm the one who'll make you laugh and cry.

Entertaining you now will be the lords of the rings,
The jumbo who sways and the canary who sings.
Come to my circus with all your things,
And feel the happiness that all this brings.

Don't hold back the tears, just let them flow
Until it's time to say goodbye and go.

The Donkey

I work as hard as anyone else
But does anyone care a damn?
Will I ever get recompense
For the loads I carry of ham?

Beast of burden I certainly am,
Considering the weight I carry.
They load me as if I was a ram
And I get no to time to tarry.

They also call me a stupid ass –
Though I'm not an ass at all.
If you were petrol but I called you 'gas',
Wouldn't that be for you a fall?

I sweat, I grind all day long,
I don't seem to cover a lot,
It's beginning now to prey on my mind –
Should I be doing something else or not?

A donkey I am, and a donkey I'll remain –
There isn't much I can do.
There are moments when you'll give me pain,
But no one else will have a clue.

I want more for less
Than the dollar I can see,
So you can keep your jumpin' dimes –
I need a life that's rich for me!

The Snake

I writhe, I slither, 'cos I'm a snake,
You feel you can't trust me for promises I make.
Metaphorically speaking I'm very well known,
Though what they say is all 'home-grown'.

I'm really fair and all up front,
Unhappy 'cos I have to bear the brunt,
There are black sheep in the herds we know,
But we're not all 'snakes' – some also glow.

Why do I strike terror in the heart?
I am magnificent with my 'hood' for a start,
There is no revulsion when you see a tiger,
So why do I induce rigor?

I try and stay away from you
And live the life for me that's true,
I'm really a grounded jungle 'bird' –
It's not my style to move in a herd.

I know I'm a very lonesome creature
But that is just a normal feature,
I don't attack the human species
Unless you tread on me, and that displeases!

I also serve a worthy cause
Please think a bit, and pause:
I do the job of the Pied Piper
Rats are scared of me 'cos I'm the viper.

Most of us are harmless, folks,
There is a little 'poison' – mainly hoax;
How else do we protect ourselves
From the rampaging elephant, and the likes of yourselves?

Look at the variety we bring to earth,
Contributing to the language you speak;
'Fork-tongued' would never have had birth
If it wasn't for me, it would be Greek.

So look at me with some kindness, friends,
I promise you I'll make amends.
I will try and keep well out of sight
So you don't suffer unnecessary fright.

I Am the Giraffe

I'm the giraffe in the zoo
With a lovely ringside view,
Nothing ever gets in my way –
I just stretch my neck and have my say.

I am a very docile creature,
Contentment is my natural feature,
Leaves are all I want to eat
And the trees are always on my beat.

No one knows how I speak,
I'm no computer geek,
No one's ever seen me laugh
'Cos I'm just the ordinary giraffe.

I can't shake hands with you, you see,
'Cos we're not on the same level, you'll agree;
I've always had to look down at you,
And that is something I'll always rue.

Friends must always good friends be,
Different heights don't matter to me;
Tall is he who stands tall
And doesn't worry about the rise and fall.

There's nothing special about me, I know,
I am just the simple average Joe,
No one comes just to see me –
So maybe I should change my zoo…
Maybe.

I Am the Camel

Deserts have ships, did you know?
Safe and sound but very slow,
They have no masts and no sails
Only short and funny tails.

I'm different from the ships at sea,
Humpback with eyes that see,
No boatswains, nor any mates,
I'm the camel, just give me dates.

Did you know there are two kinds of me
And the hump decides who,
I'm the Arabian dromedary –
I have *one*, and I'm thoroughbred too.

I am known for my loyalty
And my services to royalty,
Princes, paupers all alike,
Fancy me or take a bike.

I walk like a duck
But that aside,
If you run out of luck
I'll give you a ride.

I'll sit down for you
So you can get on,
Else you'll have no choice
And I'll be gone.

No one walks faster, not on sand,
Not for dollar or for rand,
I can walk, run or even canter,
This is serious, folks, it's not banter.

Eartha Kitt sang 'I walked a mile for her' –
You pay me well I'll do it for you, sir.
King Farouk was a personal friend
And the Sheiks of Araby love me no end.

From Egypt to Libya is a very long ride,
You'll have no problem if I'm by your side,
Time will fly, and so will I
But if you're not careful you'll be looking at the sky.

I don't care much for fallen heroes,
Won't go back for dollars with zeroes,
So hold your horses – or camel, as it were –
No one will find you, not even Ben Hur.

I'm worth my weight in solid gold
And all the stories that you've been told,
Are all very real and very true,
I may be brown, but my blood is blue!

I'm very partial to little children
I love them on my humped back,
They are so light, they weigh so little,
'Specially when I'm feeling brittle.

And now that you know so much about me,
Leave me alone and I'll thank thee,
I've a load to carry and a night to sleep –
Promise me this, this promise you'll keep.

The Mongoose and the Snake – An Imaginary Battle

How funny languages are –
From each other so very far,
In the English-speaking world I'm just a mongoose,
But the French may cook my goose.

They wouldn't understand what that was
But that doesn't matter either,
'Cos I'm just a slayer of snakes
Wherever and whatever it takes.

I'm the one who can take them on
And I love a looming battle,
The snake when he sees me wishes he'd gone
Even if he has a rattle.

The noise he makes is like the empty drum,
The rattle is an awful fake,
I could take him on, even drunk on rum –
He should flee for his own sake.

The back of the neck is where I get him
And he doesn't like it at all,
It isn't one-sided 'cos he's got vim
And he doesn't easily fall.

If you've never watched this tussle before
You've missed one hell of a lot,
We can do it again, we can act once more,
If you promise a camera shot.

Honestly speaking, I don't like the guy –
He's just too slimy for me,
He's got no legs, he's very sly
And he hates the sight of me.

Would you rather see me or him?
Make up your mind, folks,
Don't just stand on the rim –
The battle was only a hoax.

The Tortoise and the Hare

There is that old story
Of the tortoise and the hare,
Where speed may not be glory
But diligence with due care.

Measured pace is what you need
Over distance and time, my friends;
This is simple advice you must heed
As you go round life's bends.

Rest you must, but not for long,
Sporadics will get you nowhere,
You can walk the mile and sing a song
While a sprint may not get you there.

There's a lesson in this for all of us,
That life is not a racecourse,
It matters not if you ride a plane or a bus
Or if you're a thoroughbred racehorse.

The Bear

Mary had a little lamb
Whose fleece was white as snow;
I'm a bear not a ram
And I can also be white, you know,

One kind of me is the polar bear
'Cos I come from the Poles –
Not to be confused with the people there.
Where is Poland, oh where?

I'm mostly black and white,
But I come in colours too,
Brown, you know, and that's all right –
I wish I was also blue.

We're also called grizzlies
And that's my other name,
'Cos I come from the Rockies
And that gives me fame.

I roam the plains and mountains
And am a quiet sort of fellow,
Unless you eat all the plantains
And I'm just left to bellow.

You've seen me on the street
Entertaining big and small,
I can do many a feat
Like a somersault, and then stand tall.

I'm also very little
When I am the koala,
I'm carried in a pouch
But I never say, 'Ouch!'

I can be very nasty,
And gory tales you know,
But I'm not like that mostly
I'm a really nice fellow.

Remember me as 'Baloo'
In that lovely *Jungle Book* –
I'm as friendly as any of you,
From Chaplin to Robin Cook.

The Shark

I am from the family
But they never call me fish,
Just because I'm a shark
Am I not a lovely dish?

You've put me in the soup, I know –
My fins not there with me.
How can I now with the waters flow
What kind of shark will I be?

You've heard of headless horses
Now this is a finless shark!
Horses run on different courses
But for me the ocean is my park.

I'm a fairly peaceful creature,
Though very big in size,
To attack is not my feature
But I don't like your lies.

You call your own kind 'Sharks'
With no regard for form,
You should have sought my permission
You've no respect for the norm.

The connotation you give the word
Is nasty to say the least;
I wish I was a modern nerd
I'd call you a beast.

Your 'shark' is less than fair
With few or no scruples;
How can I be the equal
Of someone with so much hair?

I never ever cheat –
Deception is not my style;
If I really looked for meat
You'd have to run a mile.

I live in perfect harmony
With my friends of the sea,
I never suffer ignominy
'Cos they truly love me.

I've never played golf,
So Greg Norman I can't be;
Is he really a big bad wolf,
Or are you making up stories for me?

Please keep out of my way,
It'll be good for both of us,
Perhaps you'll see another day
And I wouldn't get called thus.

The Black Panther

I am the black panther
With eyes that brilliantly glow,
There's nothing pink about me
'Cos Peter Sellers is no more.

Besides, he couldn't walk straight,
Never mind climb a tree.
Did you ever see his funny gait?
Did he resemble me?

There's a very wild side to me
'Cos I live in Brazil, you see,
Sambas and rumbas and shaking galore
The Carnival's the place to be.

Do you know why I chose the colour black?
There's a clever side to me;
Obama's the guy, but I'm no hack,
I meld with the night, you see.

I'm also very stealthy
My feet are softly padded,
Stealth is a necessity –
The rest I've simply added.

The jungle is no place for folks
There's mercy shown to none;
When I am very hungry
You'll have to get your gun.

Or else I'll teach you a lesson
That you will never forget,
'Cos you won't be there, I promise you,
You'll be simply laid to rest.

I'm not a jumbo dumbo
Nor a screeching monkey,
'Cos I speak no mumbo-jumbo,
I'm very quiet, you see.

I can spring an awfully big surprise
Which you will never see
Until you see my glowing eyes –
And then it's too late to flee.

So it's best if you come in the day
When I am at rest,
Then you can walk all the way
And satisfy your quest.

I've never ever roamed your streets
You've never seen me there;
Why don't you leave the wilds to me
Before you're under a bear?

I can't now come to your aid
'Cos the bear's a mate of mine,
I know you are mortally scared
So I'll bid you adieu – it's time for me to dine.

Marsupial

I am a marsupial
I'm no alien, I'm real;
If you don't know the word
I can tell you I'm not a bird.

I hop on two legs –
They're not wooden pegs –
I carry a pouch
But I don't sit on a couch

I am the kangaroo
I'm Aussie too,
I move at great pace
And can beat you in a race.

I can jump very high,
Seven feet to the sky;
I box with my pals
And am friends with the gals.

You can see me Down Under
We play together in rain and thunder;
When you've seen me enough
You can pack your bags and take your stuff.